rockschool®

Guitar Grade 1

*Performance pieces, technical exercises and in-depth guidance
for Rockschool examinations*

www.rockschool.co.uk

Acknowledgements

Published by Rockschool Ltd. © 2012
Catalogue Number RSK051202
ISBN: 978-1-908920-01-0
Revision 1 | 1 November 2012 | Errata details can be found at *www.rockschool.co.uk*

AUDIO
Recorded at Fisher Lane Studios
Produced and engineered by Nick Davis
Assistant engineer and Pro Tools operator Mark Binge
Mixed and mastered at Langlei Studios
Mixing and additional editing by Duncan Jordan
Supporting Tests recorded by Duncan Jordan and Kit Morgan
Mastered by Duncan Jordan
Executive producers: James Uings, Jeremy Ward and Noam Lederman

MUSICIANS
James Arben, Joe Bennett, Jason Bowld, Larry Carlton, Stuart Clayton, Andy Crompton, Neel Dhorajiwala, Fergus Gerrand, Charlie Griffiths, Felipe Karam, Kishon Khan, Noam Lederman, DJ Harry Love, Dave Marks, Kit Morgan, Jon Musgrave, Jake Painter, Richard Pardy, Ross Stanley, Stuart Ryan, Carl Sterling, Henry Thomas, Camilo Tirado, Simon Troup, James Uings, Steve Walker, Chris Webster, Norton York, Nir Z

PUBLISHING
Fact Files written by Joe Bennett, Charlie Griffiths, Stephen Lawson, Simon Pitt, Stuart Ryan and James Uings
Walkthroughs written by James Uings
Music engraving and book layout by Simon Troup and Jennie Troup of Digital Music Art
Proof reading and copy editing by Chris Bird, Claire Davies, Stephen Lawson, Simon Pitt and James Uings
Publishing administration by Caroline Uings
Cover design by Philip Millard

SYLLABUS
Syllabus director: Jeremy Ward
Instrumental specialists: Stuart Clayton, Noam Lederman and James Uings
Special thanks to: Brad Fuller and Georg Voros

SPONSORSHIP
Noam Lederman plays Mapex Drums, PAISTE cymbals and uses Vic Firth Sticks
Rockschool would like to thank the following companies for donating instruments used in the cover artwork

PRINTING
Printed and bound in the United Kingdom by Caligraving Ltd
CDs manufactured in the European Union by Software Logistics

DISTRIBUTION
Exclusive Distributors: Music Sales Ltd

CONTACTING ROCKSCHOOL
www.rockschool.co.uk
Telephone: +44 (0)845 460 4747
Fax: +44 (0)845 460 1960

Table of Contents

Introductions & Information

Rockschool Grade Pieces

Technical Exercises

Supporting Tests

Additional Information

Welcome to Rockschool Guitar Grade 1

Welcome to Guitar Grade 1

Welcome to the Rockschool Guitar Grade 1 pack. This book and CD contain everything you need to play guitar at this grade. In the book you will find the exam scores in both standard guitar notation and TAB. The CD has full stereo mixes of each tune, backing tracks to play along to for practice, and spoken two bar count-ins to both the full mixes and backing track versions of the songs.

Guitar Exams

At each grade, you have the option of taking one of two different types of examination:

- **Grade Exam:** a Grade Exam is a mixture of music performances, technical work and tests. You prepare three pieces (two of which may be Free Choice Pieces) and the contents of the Technical Exercise section. This accounts for 75% of the exam marks. The other 25% consists of: *either* a Sight Reading *or* an Improvisation & Interpretation test (10%), a pair of instrument specific Ear Tests (10%), and finally you will be asked five General Musicianship Questions (5%). The pass mark is 60%.

- **Performance Certificate:** in a Performance Certificate you play five pieces. Up to three of these can be Free Choice Pieces. Each song is marked out of 20 and the pass mark is 60%.

Book Contents

The book is divided into a number of sections. These are:

- **Exam Pieces:** in this book you will find six specially commissioned pieces of Grade 1 standard. Each of these is preceded by a *Fact File*. Each Fact File contains a summary of the song, its style, tempo, key and technical features, along with a list of the musicians who played on it. There is additional information on the techniques and style as well as recommended further listening. The song is printed on two pages. Immediately after each song is a *Walkthrough*. This covers the song from a performance perspective, focusing on the technical issues you will encounter along the way. Each Walkthrough features two graphical musical 'highlights' showing particular parts of the song. Each song comes with a full mix version and a backing track. Both versions have spoken count-ins at the beginning. Please note that any solos played on the full mix versions are indicative only.

- **Technical Exercises:** you should prepare the exercises set in this grade in the keys indicated. There is also a Riff test which should be practised and played to the backing track.

- **Supporting Tests and General Musicianship Questions:** in Guitar Grade 1 there are three supporting tests – *either* a Sight Reading *or* an Improvisation & Interpretation test and two Ear Tests – and a set of General Musicianship Questions (GMQs) asked at the end of each exam. Examples of the types of tests likely to appear in the exam are printed in this book. Additional test examples of both types of test and the GMQs can be found in the Rockschool *Guitar Companion Guide*.

- **Grade 2 Preview:** in this book we have included one of the songs found in the Grade 2 Guitar book as a taster. The piece is printed with its Fact File and Walkthrough and the full mix can be found on the CD.

- **General Information:** finally, you will find information on exam procedures, including online examination entry, marking schemes, and what to do when arriving, and waiting, for your exam.

We hope you enjoy using this book. You will find a *Syllabus Guide* for Guitar and other exam information on our website: *www.rockschool.co.uk*. Rockschool Graded Music Exams are accredited in England, Wales and Northern Ireland by Ofqual, the DfE and CCEA and by SQA Accreditation in Scotland.

SONG TITLE: GET OFF

GENRE: INDIE

TEMPO: 115 BPM

KEY: A MINOR

TECH FEATURES: ACCENTS

STACCATO NOTES

SYNCOPATION

COMPOSER: JAMES UINGS

PERSONNEL: STUART RYAN (GTR)

HENRY THOMAS (BASS)

NOAM LEDERMAN (DRUMS)

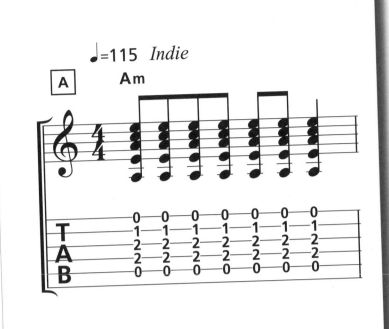

OVERVIEW

'Get Off' is written in an indie style that will be of interest to fans of bands like Arctic Monkeys, The Libertines and The Strokes. This type of indie music is characterised by energy, attack and a generally loose feel. 'Get Off' is split into several sections: an intro composed of open chords, a single-note riff on the bass strings and a lead melody line involving some string skipping.

STYLE FOCUS

The energy and attack of these kinds of bands can be difficult to capture. It comes from the picking hand: this should be loose but needs to strike the strings with a 'snapping' motion from the wrist so that you can hit the strings harder. Another challenge when playing this style is the abrupt, 'stop start' nature of the riffs. In this piece, this is characterised by the staccato notes and the rests that occur in the riff starting at bar four. Accurate muting is a must here.

THE BIGGER PICTURE

'Indie' (independent) music is a style that developed in the UK from the 1980s onwards.

Although it focuses primarily on rhythm guitar and riff building, there have been some creative guitarists within the genre, most notably Jonny Marr of The Smiths and John Squire of The Stone Roses. Indie guitar is generally quite textural and can involve everything from clean arpeggiated chords to spiky, angular distorted riffs. One of the most popular groups within the genre currently are Arctic Monkeys. Since forming in Sheffield, England in 2002, the four-piece have achieved worldwide fame with their energetic fusion of punk, indie and rock styles. Their angular riffs and energetic higher tempos have set them apart from their contemporaries and although they don't write particularly complex guitar parts, they intertwine well and drive the music forward.

RECOMMENDED LISTENING

The Arctic Monkeys' debut album *Whatever People Say I Am, That's What I'm Not* (2006) remains the fastest-selling debut by a band, thanks to the songs 'I Bet You Look Good On The Dancefloor', 'When The Sun Goes Down' and 'Fake Tales Of San Francisco'. Other key groups include The Libertines, Oasis, Radiohead and Blur. The Strokes sparked a resurgence of the genre in America upon the release of their debut album *Is This It* (2001), which has influenced many current indie bands.

Get Off

James Uings

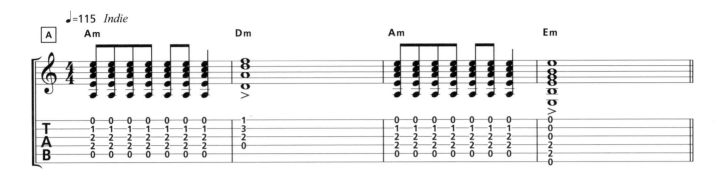

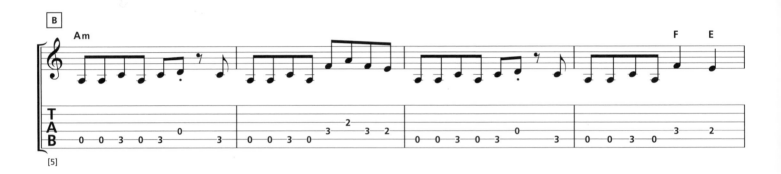

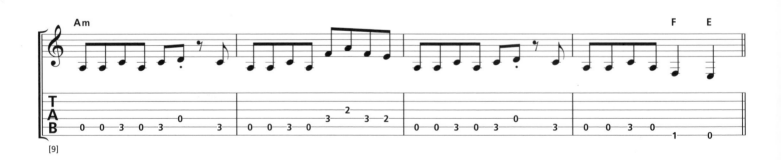

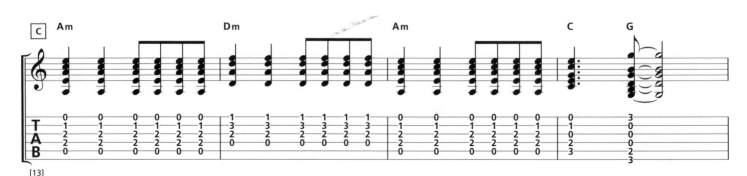

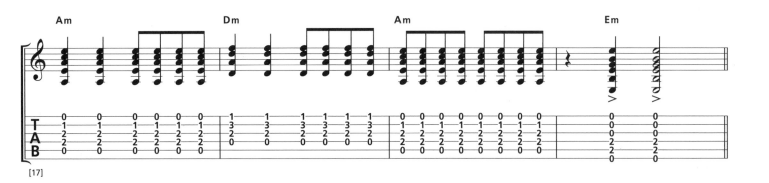

[17]

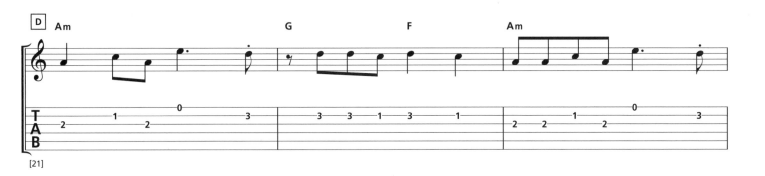

[21]

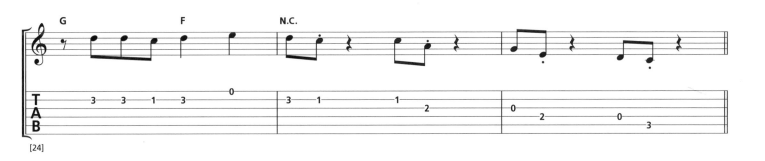

[24]

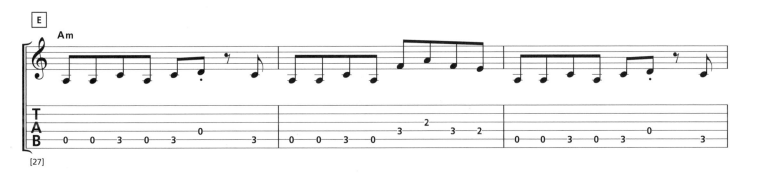

[27]

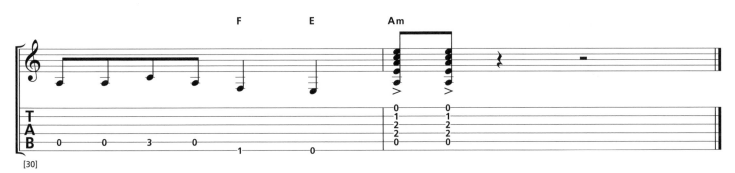

[30]

Walkthrough

Amp Settings
Your tone for this track should be biting and aggressive. Use an overdrive that's set so that the sound is breaking up but not too saturated. Too much gain or using a metal-style distortion will make the sound too mushy and will actually reduce the punch and aggression found in this style of music. Boost the middle a little to give your tone some edge.

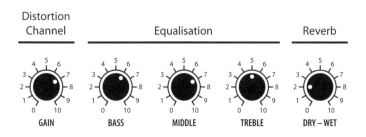

A Section (Bars 1–4)
This intro section creates an immediate impact by contrasting aggressively strummed chords with single, accented chord hits.

Bar 2 | *Accent*
An accent sign is placed above or below a note head. There are five different kinds of accent sign, but by far the most common is the one used in this piece and shown below the D minor chord in bar 2. When you see this sign, you should accent the marked note by playing it slightly louder than the other notes in the phrase.

B Section (Bars 5–12)
The B section is made up of an open position, single-note riff that uses mostly eighth notes.

Bars 5–12 | *Alternate picking*
Using all downstrokes can make the sound more consistent; however, there is a lot of wasted motion that can make playing the riff at this tempo quite demanding. You may find alternate picking (down and upstrokes) a more efficient and less fatiguing way to play this riff (Fig. 1).

Bar 5 | *Staccato open strings*
These staccato open strings are more tricky than most notes or chords that are marked staccato because you can't simply release pressure on the strings to mute them. To mute this you can either use the underside of your fretting hand fingers or place the edge of your picking hand on the string.

C Section (Bars 13–20)
This section of 'Get Off' features strummed open chords which end with two accented E minor chords that lead into the next section.

Bars 13–20 | *Constant strumming motion*
Your strumming hand should move in a constant down up, eighth-note pattern, even when it's not hitting the strings; these are called 'ghost' strokes. This technique will help build your sense of timing and make your rhythm parts more fluent. Fig. 2 shows the strumming directions with the ghost strokes identified in brackets.

D and E Sections (Bars 21–31)
The D section is a driving single-note melody based in open position and features a small amount of syncopation and string skipping. The E section is a reprise of the B section and serves to bring the song to a close.

Bars 21–24 | *Syncopation*
A syncopated part is one that accents the weaker beats in a bar. This can look complicated on paper but is actually quite a natural sounding rhythm; syncopation is common in modern music and, therefore, is not an unusual sound. The melody has a catchy groove and you should be able to 'feel' where the notes go instinctively. If you find this difficult, count the eighth notes in the bar and work out exactly where each note lands before gradually building up the speed until you are comfortable.

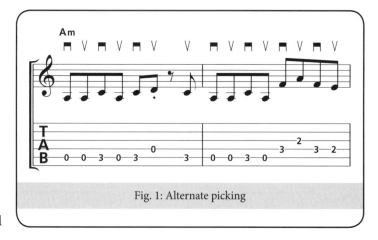

Fig. 1: Alternate picking

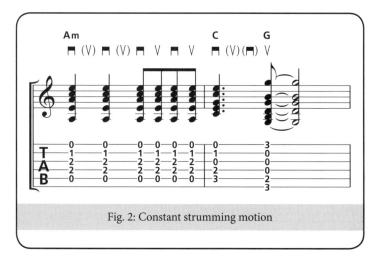

Fig. 2: Constant strumming motion

SONG TITLE: UMBRA BELLA

GENRE: GUITAR INSTRUMENTAL

TEMPO: 130 BPM

KEY: D MINOR

TECH FEATURES: OPEN CHORDS

LEAD MELODY PLAYING

WIDE STRETCHES

COMPOSER: SIMON TROUP

PERSONNEL: STUART RYAN (GTR)

HENRY THOMAS (BASS)

NOAM LEDERMAN (DRUMS)

ROSS STANLEY (KEYS)

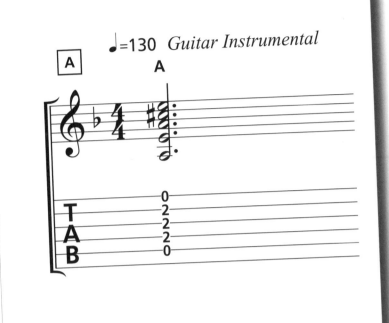

♩=130 *Guitar Instrumental*

OVERVIEW

'Umbra Bella' is an homage to The Shadows, a legendary British instrumental pop group who formed in the 1950s. In keeping with the style of the group, the lead guitar plays a melody line interspersed with some strummed and arpeggiated (notes are picked individually) open chords. Clean playing is essential here, as is good timing.

STYLE FOCUS

Hank Marvin, the lead guitarist with The Shadows, was a pivotal figure in shaping the sound of guitar in the 1950s and 1960s. He was one of the first guitarists in the UK to play a Fender Stratocaster, and his unique use and control of the tremelo arm made him stand apart from his contemporaries, many of whom were simply strumming acoustic guitars. The ability to play the melody cleanly in 'Umbra Bella' is essential and you should focus on dynamics, tone and timing.

THE BIGGER PICTURE

Marvin's guitar playing was revolutionary at the time, and he is renowned for playing with a great touch and a bright clean tone. The Shadows were an instrumental group who were notable for backing pop singer Cliff Richard, but the tale doesn't end there. The Shadows also achieved great success in their own right with a string of instrumental hits. Instrumental guitar music flourished through the surf guitar sound of 1950s American groups, with The Ventures and The Shadows adding their own twist. Marvin developed a unique guitar sound based on his use of the vibrato, or tremolo arm, on his Fender Stratocaster and the echo devices that made his notes repeat after he had played them. The Shadows' catchy melodies and driving rhythms helped them carve out their own sound that was distinctive from anything else around at the time. It is unusual now for instrumental groups to have top 10 hits, and The Shadows remain one of the most successful instrumental groups of the last 50 years.

RECOMMENDED LISTENING

The Shadow's version of 'Apache' features many elements of the group's sound, especially the tremolo and echo-drenched lead guitar melody set against the propulsive acoustic guitar strumming of rhythm player Bruce Welch. Other Shadows classics include 'FBI', 'Wonderful Land' and 'Guitar Tango.' Their playing on Cliff Richards' 'Summer Holiday' also contains one of the iconic licks of 1960s pop.

Umbra Bella

Simon Troup

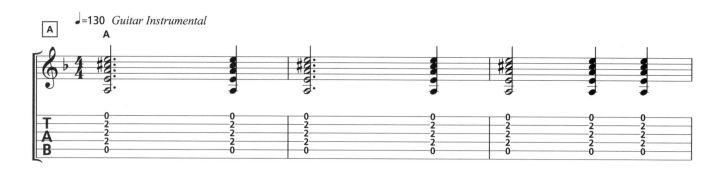

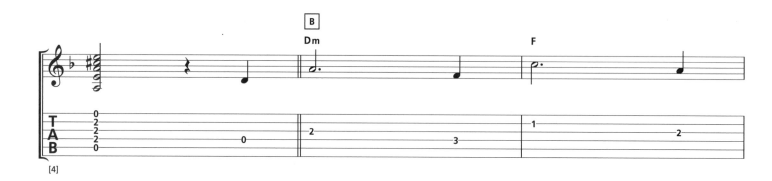

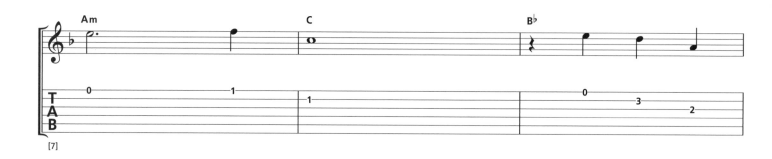

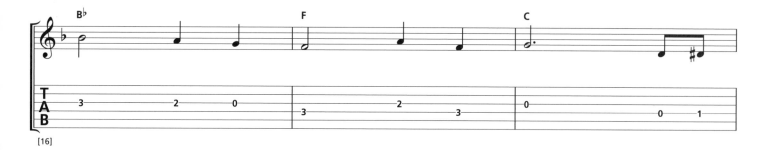

[16]

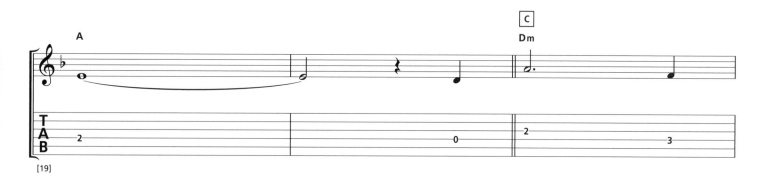

[19]

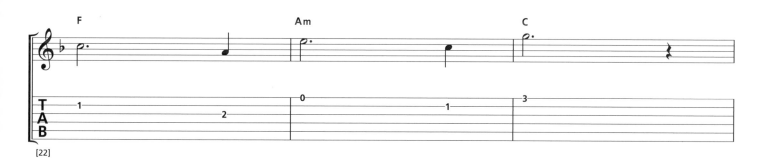

[22]

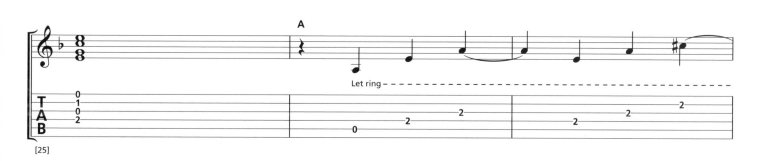

[25]

[28]

Walkthrough

Amp Settings

A bright, clean sound is ideal for the guitar part in 'Umbra Bella'. Adding distortion would affect the clarity of the part and would sound out of place in this style. Even clean channels can distort, so keep the gain low to achieve a pure tone. If you have access to it, adding reverb to the sound will help you get closer to the classic Shadows tone.

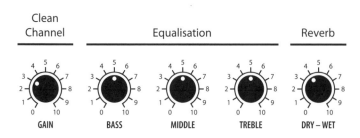

A Section (Bars 1–4)

The intro of this tune is based on an open A chord that works to create tension in anticipation of the main melody found in the B section.

Bars 1–4 | *Strumming chords*

Aim to keep your wrist relaxed here and allow the pick to travel lightly across the strings to achieve a satisfactory strumming action. It is common for beginners to 'dig in' too much and drag the pick across the strings so that individual strings can be heard. Be careful to avoid this.

Bars 1–4 | *Counting rhythms*

With a relatively high-paced track such as this, counting the beats along with the music can be a helpful way of making sure you play the chords in the correct rhythm. As you count, make sure that the chords you play coincide exactly with the numbers you are counting (Fig. 1).

B Section (Bars 5–20)

The B section is a single-note melody that, at first glance, looks simple. However, the high tempo and wide interval leaps make this section more of a challenge to play than it first appears.

Bars 5–7 | *Wide intervals*

Wide intervals present some technical challenges. In particular, skipping strings will require some practice to play accurately. Start slowly, concentrating on playing accurately. Only increase the speed of your playing when you can play at your current tempo without error. Wide intervals usually mean the melody notes will be on different strings, and as a result they can bleed into each other if allowed to ring on. Make sure you release any fretted notes before the next melody note is played.

Bar 15 | *Wide stretch*

This bar features a four fret stretch in open position. It's important that you use your fourth finger to fret the E♭ at the 4th fret of the B string (Fig. 2). While this may feel difficult at first, the strength in your fourth finger will increase quickly with practice.

C Section (Bars 21–30)

This is a reprise of the B section, then the A section. It features variations of the main melody and varies the intro by playing an arpeggiated A major chord rather than a strummed part.

Bars 26–28 | *Arpeggios*

If the notes in a chord are picked one at a time, the chord is being 'arpeggiated'.

Bars 26–28 | *Chord accuracy*

It is important to fret chords accurately, and the arpeggiated chords in bars 26–28 will expose any notes that are not fretted cleanly. Fret with the tips of your fingers to make room for the adjacent higher sounding strings to ring clearly. If you have difficulty, experiment with the position of your thumb, which has a large impact on your hand's mobility.

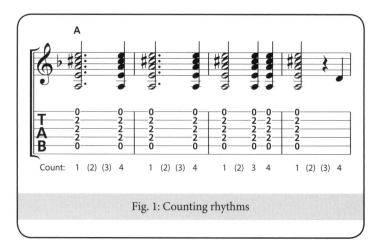

Fig. 1: Counting rhythms

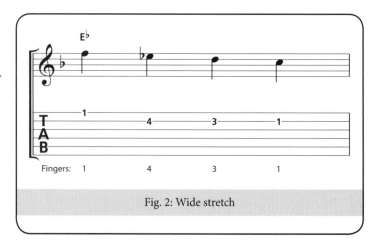

Fig. 2: Wide stretch

Just Don't Know

SONG TITLE: JUST DON'T KNOW

GENRE: CLASSIC ROCK

TEMPO: 90 BPM

KEY: A MINOR

TECH FEATURES: POWERCHORDS
SLIDES
TIED RHYTHMS

COMPOSER: KIT MORGAN

PERSONNEL: STUART RYAN (GTR)
HENRY THOMAS (BASS)
NOAM LEDERMAN (DRUMS)

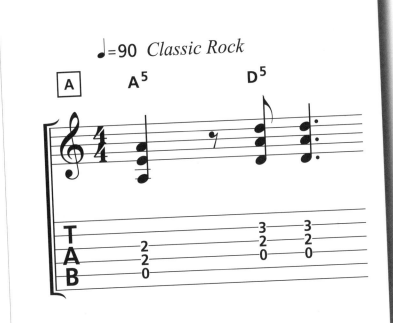

OVERVIEW

'Just Don't Know' is a classic rock tinged song that pays tribute to pioneering groups of the 1970s like Led Zeppelin, AC/DC and Thin Lizzy. The track features many hallmarks of this style, including crunchy open position powerchords and ideas drawn from the minor pentatonic scale. Attack and precision are some key components for success within this style.

STYLE FOCUS

Classic rock developed in the 1970s through the influence of guitarists like Led Zeppelin's Jimmy Page, AC/DC's Angus Young and Thin Lizzy's Scott Gorham. These bands often featured two guitars (rhythm and lead) or one guitar player holding down riffs then soloing (e.g. Jimmy Page and Black Sabbath's Tony Iommi). You will encounter many key elements of the latter type of player here as you move from powerchord based ideas to open string riffs and a melody/lead line.

THE BIGGER PICTURE

In the classic rock format the guitarist is often adept at both lead and rhythm playing, although there are scenarios where there are two guitarists. A classic example is AC/DC, where Malcolm Young holds down the rhythm parts while his brother Angus always takes the lead. Groups like Thin Lizzy exploited the possibilities of having two guitarists by creating intricate harmonized lead guitar parts where both guitars played simultaneously. Riff building and soloing with the minor pentatonic scale are key components of classic rock guitar, and you will find this scale in abundance in the music of all the aforementioned groups. Picking hand attack is important here: in the 1970s, high gain amps did not exist so the guitarist obtained more gain (distortion) from the amplifier by turning it up loud and hitting the strings hard.

RECOMMENDED LISTENING

Getting into classic rock is easy thanks to a wealth of great material. Essential listening includes AC/DC's *Highway To Hell* (1979), *Led Zeppelin IV* (1971), featuring the legendary 'Stairway to Heaven', and Thin Lizzy's *Jailbreak* album (1976). Further listening comes in the form of Aerosmith and Van Halen, who took rock in a more technical, lead guitar focused direction (especially Van Halen) thanks to pioneering guitarist Edward Van Halen who was a master of both lead and rhythm guitar.

Guitar Grade 1

13

Just Don't Know

Kit Morgan

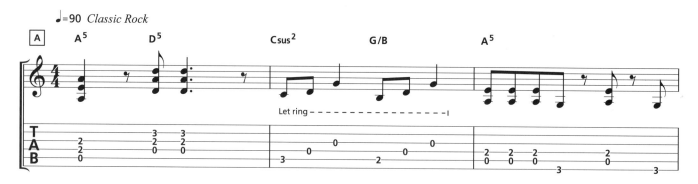

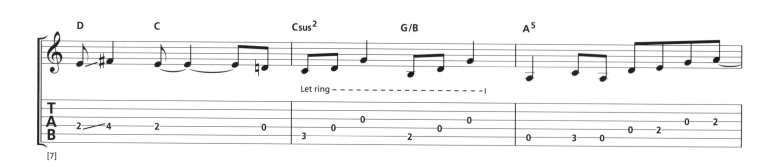

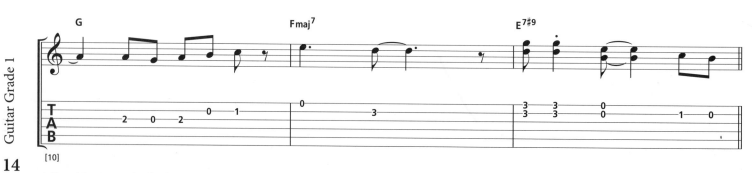

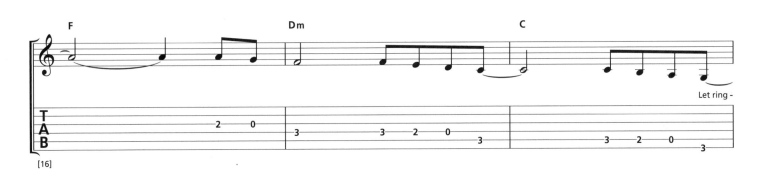

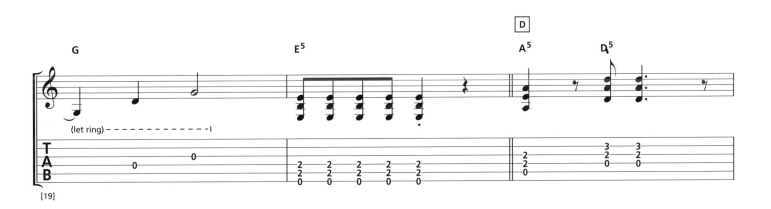

Walkthrough

Amp Settings

The key part of a classic rock guitar tone is the middle. This is usually boosted to give the guitar an aggressive sound that cuts through the rest of the band. Lead guitar particularly benefits from this approach. You should use an overdrive with the gain set to around 7, but be careful not to add too much gain because you need clarity as well as grit.

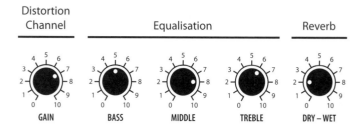

A Section (Bars 1–4)

The A section is an open position riff that uses a combination of powerchords, single notes and ringing chords that use open strings.

Bar 2 | *Let ring*

Usually in a single note melody, you should avoid letting the notes 'bleed' into each other because this can affect the clarity of the part. In this case, however, the melody is based on the notes of a chord ringing into each other, hence the self-explanatory 'Let ring' indication.

Bar 3 | *Syncopation*

When a part accents the weaker beats in the bar (usually the '&' of each beat), this is known as syncopation. The rhythm in bar 3 may appear intimidating, but it's quite easy once you spend some time on it. One approach is to work out where each note falls in the bar and count "1 & 2 & 3 & 4 &" as you play. Start slowly and only increase speed when ready.

B Section (Bars 5–12)

This section features single note riffs and double-stops, and contains a reprise of the ringing chords from the A section.

Bar 7 | *Slide*

Pick the first note of bar 7 and then, without re-picking the string, slide up to the F♯ at the 4th fret of the same string. As you slide up, make sure you maintain pressure into the neck to keep the note ringing. It's common for people to rush the slide but you should take time to ensure that the first note sounds for a full eighth note (Fig. 1).

C & D Sections (Bars 13–24)

The majority of this section is a single-note melody using a tied rhythm. The section ends with a powerchord that dramatically sets up the D section, which is a reprise of the opening A section.

Bars 13–19 | *Tied rhythms*

When two notes of the same pitch are joined by a tie (not to be confused with a slur marking), only the first note is played. However, you should hold the note for the duration of *both* notes. If tied notes are new to you work on the phrase slowly, counting as you play (Fig. 2).

Bar 20 | *Staccato*

The staccato note on beat three of bar 20 (marked with a dot) should be articulated by releasing pressure on the strings. Don't take your fingers all the way off the string because this will slow you down and may produce unwanted string noise. Instead, just stop pressing. This chord is more tricky than most notes or chords that are marked staccato because the open string will ring on. To mute this, either use the underside of your fretting hand fingers or place the edge of your picking hand on the string.

Bar 24 | *Note lengths*

When a song ends it can be tempting to let the final note ring on for longer than notated. Be sure to stop the final note after one beat.

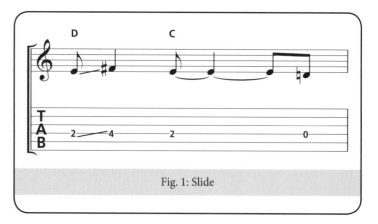

Fig. 1: Slide

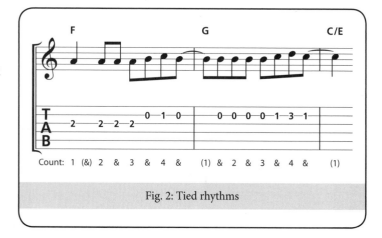

Fig. 2: Tied rhythms

SONG TITLE: KRAUSS COUNTRY
GENRE: COUNTRY
TEMPO: 88 BPM
KEY: C MAJOR

TECH FEATURES: OPEN CHORDS
DOUBLE-STOPS
LEAD MELODY PLAYING

COMPOSER: DEIDRE CARTWRIGHT

PERSONNEL: STUART RYAN (GTR)
HENRY THOMAS (BASS)
NOAM LEDERMAN (DRUMS)

OVERVIEW

'Krauss Country' is a composition written in the style of American bluegrass/country singer Alison Krauss. The guitar plays a melody line on single strings, which is then harmonised with double-stops. This is a common technique in country guitar.

STYLE FOCUS

Bluegrass music, a close cousin of country, is the folk music of America and can be fast and furious or soft and lyrical, as is the case with 'Krauss Country.' Bluegrass and country tunes are often played instrumentally, with one instrument taking the melody. In this case the guitar plays a simple melodic figure, which is then developed with double-stops where you play two notes simultaneously to create harmony. Major and minor thirds are particularly common harmonies in bluegrass and country. Make sure you listen to the backing track to hear the complementary guitar parts.

THE BIGGER PICTURE

Country music is popular in the United States and has a long, rich heritage. Today there are several branches of the style from modern country rock of Garth Brooks and Keith Urban to the more traditional bluegrass artists such as singer and violinist Alison Krauss. Bluegrass musicians are often virtuoso players who are comfortable playing at high speeds. A typical bluegrass band may use a combination of guitar, mandolin, fiddle (violin), dobro (slide guitar), double bass, mandolin, banjo and vocals. It is unusual to find drums in bluegrass, but they are usually found in the majority of country music groups. Alison Krauss and her band Union Station are regarded as the leaders in this field of country, thanks to their exciting readings of traditional bluegrass along with modern country. Bluegrass guitarists use acoustic instruments and either flatpick (use a plectrum) or fingerpick with the picking hand.

RECOMMENDED LISTENING

Alison Krauss and Union Station's *Live* (2002) is where you will hear a tight bluegrass band at their best. They are also masters of slower ballads, which serve to create a contrasting dynamic. Bluegrass guitar player Tony Rice is also highly regarded within the bluegrass genre, and his album *58597 The Bluegrass Guitar Collection* (2003) represents this modern master perfectly. Finally, listen to the grandfather of bluegrass, mandolinist Bill Monroe.

Krauss Country

Deirdre Cartwright

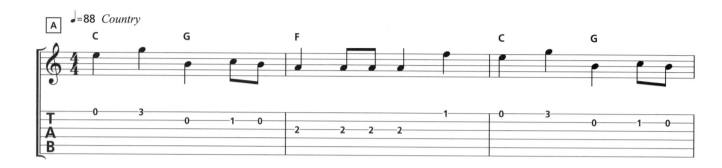

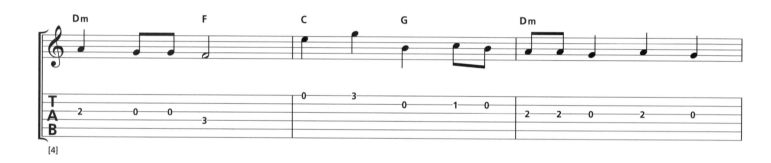

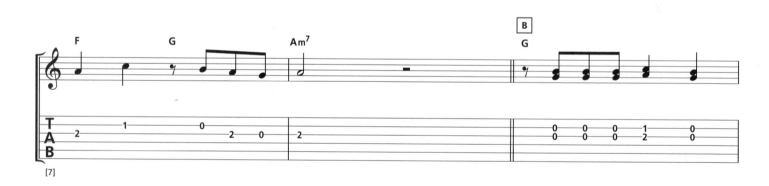

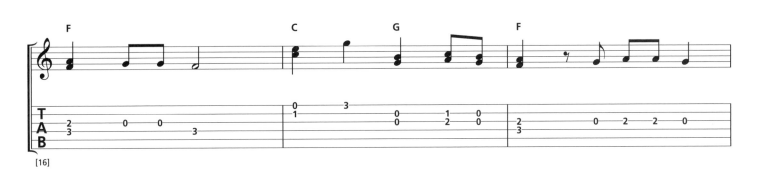

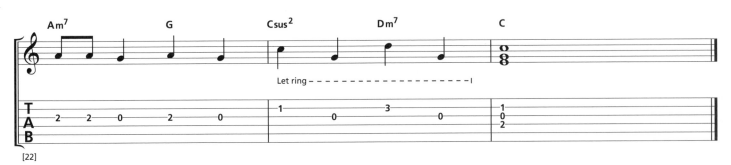

Guitar Grade 1

Walkthrough

Amp Settings

Aim for a warm, full and clean tone on this track. The choice of pickup is up to you, but selecting one located nearer the neck will give you the warmest tone. Boost the bass a little and, if your tone is still too bright, roll off a small amount of treble and middle. A modest amount of reverb will add some ambience to the song's melody.

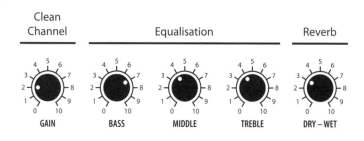

A Section (Bars 1–8)

The A section is a flowing, single-note melody based on the C major scale. It features repeated notes, a wide interval string skip and an eighth-note rest.

Bars 2–3 | *Wide intervals*

Wide intervals present some technical challenges. In particular, skipping strings requires accurate picking. Start slowly and only increase speed when you can play at your current tempo without error. Wide intervals usually mean the melody notes will be on different strings, and as a result they can bleed into one other if allowed to ring on. Release any fretted notes before the next melody note is played.

Bar 7 | *Eighth-note rest*

The eighth-note rest in bar 7 can be tricky to execute at first. Count the bar in eighth notes: "1 & 2 & 3 & 4 &". The first two notes should be played when you say "1" and "2" respectively. The third note should be played after the eighth-note rest on the '&' of beat three (Fig. 1).

B Section (Bars 9–12)

The B section melody is based on double-stops. The final bar is a descending line that leads into the C section.

Bars 9–11 | *Double-stops*

A double-stop is two notes played at the same time. The challenge here is to make sure both notes ring out clearly. Using the tips of your fingers to fret the notes will make it easier to play the notes cleanly and prevent the underside of the finger playing the G string from muting the B string. Check both notes are ringing by picking them individually.

Bar 10 | *Fingering options*

It is possible to play this phrase using your first and second fingers to fret the first double-stop, and the third and fourth fingers to play the second. However, you may prefer to move the fingerboard shape two frets higher and then move back down (Fig. 2). Make sure this movement is clean and don't slide from one double-stop to the next.

C Section (Bars 13–24)

This is a reprise of the A section melody. This time, many of the notes are harmonised and played as double-stops.

Bar 17 | *Fretting accuracy*

Playing the C note on the first fret of the B string with the tip of your first finger will allow you to arch your finger over the E string so that it can ring freely. At times it can be difficult to hear if both double-stop notes are ringing clearly, so pick them individually to make sure.

Bar 19 | *Note lengths*

The F note from the double-stop in beat one needs to stop sounding when you play the double-stop in beat two. Release the pressure on the string as you play the next double-stop or it will ring on, meaning the end result will be closer to the sound of a chord than a double-stop melody.

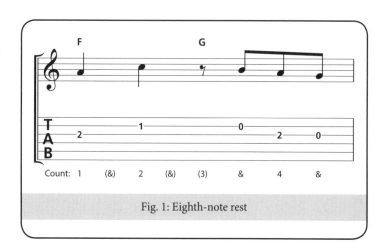

Fig. 1: Eighth-note rest

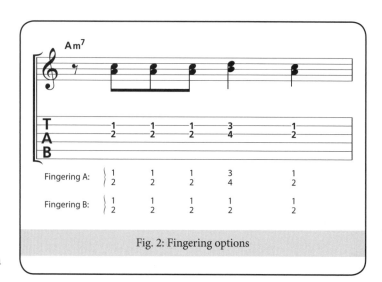

Fig. 2: Fingering options

SONG TITLE: ICAUFO

GENRE: ROCK

TEMPO: 98 BPM

KEY: E MINOR

TECH FEATURES: CROSS-PICKING

DOUBLESTOPS

COUNTING RHYTHMS

COMPOSER: JOE BENNETT

PERSONNEL: STUART RYAN (GTR)

HENRY THOMAS (BASS)

NOAM LEDERMAN (DRUMS)

JOE BENNETT (KEYS)

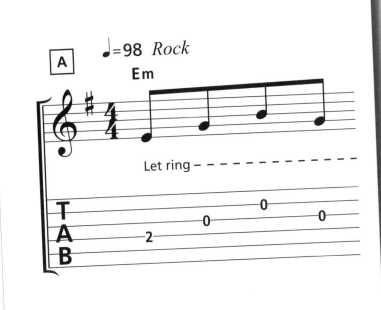

OVERVIEW

'ICAUFO' is a melodic rock piece influenced by bands in the vein of Foo Fighters and Biffy Clyro. It uses cross-picked arpeggios, meaning that the notes of a chord are played one by one and allowed to 'let ring'. These can be played with plectrum or fingers.

STYLE FOCUS

In this style of music the chord shapes may be simple but can feature accidentals (notes that are not part of the home key, which in this case is E minor). As a result there are sometimes new fingerings and positions, such as the note of C♯ that appears in bar 3. The guitar can play either a lead or an accompaniment role. Here, for the first eight bars it provides a backdrop for the violin's melody then takes centre stage for the double-stopped solo at bar 9.

Mid-tempo rock tracks like this focus on quavers, or eighth notes, but these should be played differently depending on context. Cross-picked arpeggios are usually played with alternating up and down pick strokes to provide smooth, fluent and even quavers. Double-stopped solos usually benefit from the aggressive sound provided by playing all downstrokes. Because melodic rock often goes beyond simple powerchords, it's important to fret the shapes cleanly and accurately. In particular, focus on letting the open strings ring out clearly.

THE BIGGER PICTURE

Melodic rock kicked off in the late 1960s when The Beatles, The Doors and others were experimenting in their songwriting and recording techniques. Increased success led to bigger recording budgets and it became commonplace for successful bands to develop complex arrangements and song structures, and to work with orchestras. This combination of a big sound, traditional song structures and powerful melodies has been adopted by dozens of rock bands including Deep Purple, Queen, Rush, Big Star, Pixies, Incubus and Matchbox Twenty.

RECOMMENDED LISTENING

For powerful melodic rock with cross-picked arpeggios and a descending chord sequence, start with The Beatles' 'While My Guitar Gently Weeps'. Led Zeppelin's 'Stairway To Heaven' uses similar let ring techniques. More recently, similar techniques are prominent on Foo Fighters' 'These Days' and Biffy Clyro's 'Know Your Quarry'.

ICAUFO

Joe Bennett

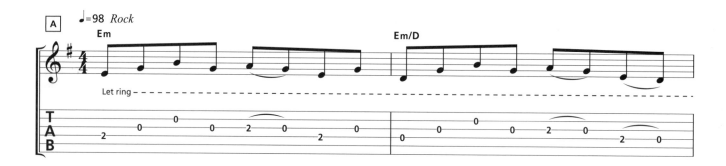

[3]

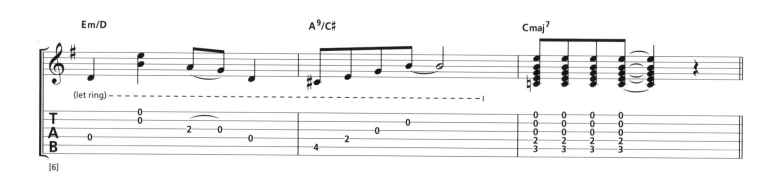

[6]

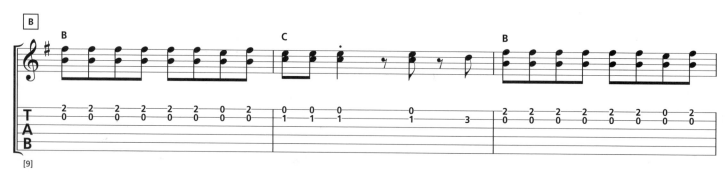

[9]

© Copyright 2012 Rock School Ltd.

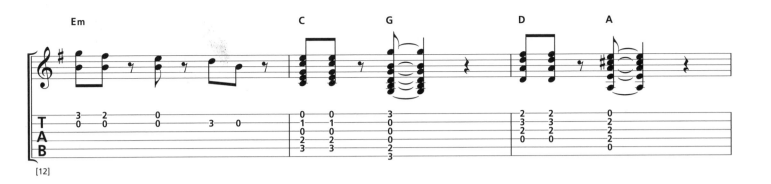

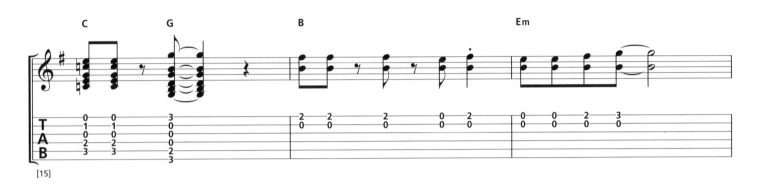

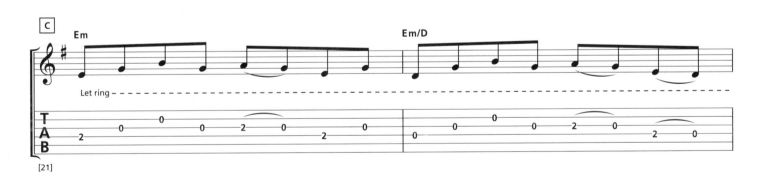

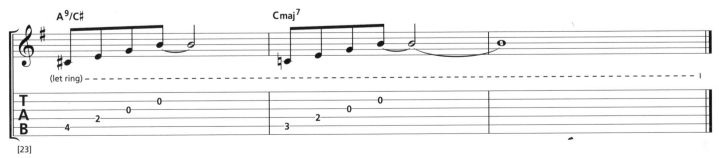

Guitar Grade 1

23

Walkthrough

Amp Settings

You are aiming for a slightly overdriven sound that's only just breaking up. Set the gain to a low setting and be careful that there's only a small amount of distortion or the part will lack clarity. Boost the middle and treble to give your tone some edge. Adding some reverb, where available, will help the notes of the arpeggiated chords flow, but be careful not to add too much or you risk drowning the guitar.

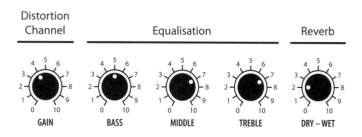

A Section (Bars 1–8)

This section is a riff / melody that combines arpeggiated chords, pull-offs and strummed chords.

Bars 1–4 | *Arpeggiated chords*

When the notes of a chord are played individually this is known as an arpeggio. When the notes of a chord are picked individually (usually to let them ring into each other) the chords are being 'arpeggiated'.

Bars 1–7 | *Let ring*

Often in a single-note melody you should avoid letting the notes 'bleed' into one other because this can affect the clarity of the part. In this case, however, the melody is based on the notes of a chord ringing into each other, hence the self-explanatory 'Let ring' indication.

Bar 1 | *Pull-off*

The pull-off is indicated by the curved line seen in beat 3 (it is also present in bar 2). Play the first note and then, without picking, pull your finger off the string and towards the floor in a snapping motion.

Bars 1–8 | *Complex chord names*

Many of the chords in this piece have complex names that, on the surface at least, may look intimidating. However, these chords are either open chord shapes with one finger added or removed, or they are simple fretboard patterns that are combined with open strings to produce exotic chords that are easy to play, sound good and have sophisticated names.

Bars 1–8 | *Fretting accuracy*

Fret the notes of this riff with the tips of your fingers because there is a danger that the fingers fretting the lower sounding strings will mute the higher sounding ones. If you have

difficulty with this, experiment with the position of your thumb which has a large impact on your hand's mobility.

B & C Sections (Bars 9–25)

The B section consists of a double-stop melody played on the E and B strings. There are also some rhythmic open position chords. The C section is essentially a reprise of part of the A section.

Bar 10 | *Counting rhythms*

Bar 9 is quite an easy rhythm to pick up by ear, but if you find it difficult try counting the bar slowly in eighth notes ("1 & 2 & 3 & 4 &") and carefully place the notes at the right time (Fig. 1). Only increase the speed when you feel comfortable with the part.

Bars 9–20 | *Double-stops*

A double-stop is two notes played at the same time (Fig. 2). The challenge here is to make sure both notes ring out clearly. Using the tips of your fingers to fret the notes will make it easier to play the notes cleanly and prevent the underside of the finger playing the B string from muting the E string. You can check that both notes are ringing by picking them individually.

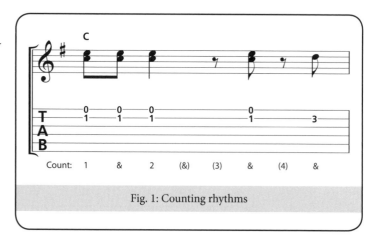

Fig. 1: Counting rhythms

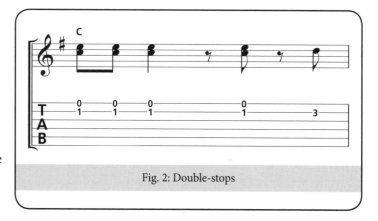

Fig. 2: Double-stops

SONG TITLE: FAB STOMP

GENRE: 60S POP

TEMPO: 120 BPM

KEY: D MAJOR

TECH FEATURES: STRUMMED CHORDS
DOUBLE-STOPS
SIMPLE SYNCOPATION

COMPOSER: DEIRDRE CARTWRIGHT

PERSONNEL: STUART RYAN (GTR)
HENRY THOMAS (BASS)
NOAM LEDERMAN (DRUMS)

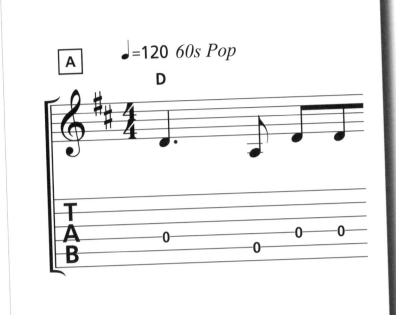

OVERVIEW

'Fab Stomp' is an example of 1960s pop in the style of groups like The Dave Clark 5, The Hollies and Freddie And The Dreamers. It features a mixture of strummed first position chords and a melody line. The technical challenges in this song are to count the dotted notes and the rests, and to keep the strummed chords even. There are also double-stops (two notes played at the same time), which are a common feature within this style of music.

STYLE FOCUS

Early to mid 1960s British pop music followed the model used by The Beatles: two guitars, and often more than one vocalist performing up-tempo, good-time, melodic songs written in major keys. Some of the songs were written by the bands themselves, although most were written either by professional 'Tin Pan Alley' songwriters, or were cover versions of songs made famous previously by American artists.

THE BIGGER PICTURE

Global Beatlemania in 1963 and 1964 opened the door to fame for 'beat combos' from different parts of Britain, particularly from Manchester and London. The cream of these bands joined The Beatles by going to America and were part of the 'British Invasion' that was to last for most of the 1960s. Foremost among this collection of groups were the hugely successful Mancunian bands The Hollies, Freddie And The Dreamers and Wayne Fontana, who, along with London's The Dave Clark Five (or 'The DC5' as they were often known), followed The Beatles to America. The DC5 were the second British band to appear on the Ed Sullivan Show, which was seen as a springboard to fame and success in the USA.

RECOMMENDED LISTENING

The Dave Clark Five's first number one, 'Glad All Over', knocked The Beatles' 'I Wanna Hold Your Hand' off the top of the British singles chart in January 1964. The Hollies' first top 10 hit was 'Stay', released in the same year, and was followed by 'Just One Look' and 'Carrie Anne' among other hits. Freddie And The Dreamers' frontman, Freddie Garrity, brought a range of eccentric dance moves to their performances that were very much a part of the band's appeal. This can be seen to great effect on surviving clips of the band performing their hits including 'You Were Made for Me', 'I'm Telling You Now' and 'I Understand' in their heyday.

Guitar Grade 1

25

Fab Stomp

Deirdre Cartwright

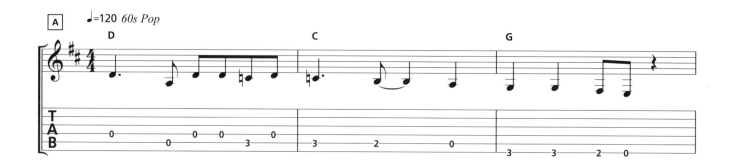

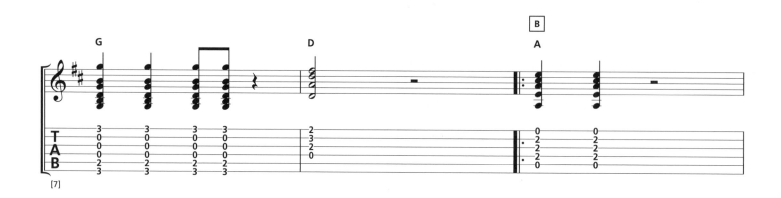

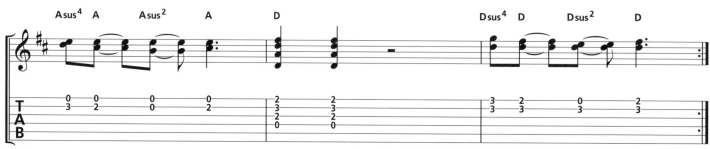

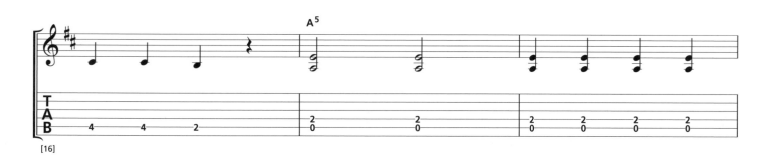

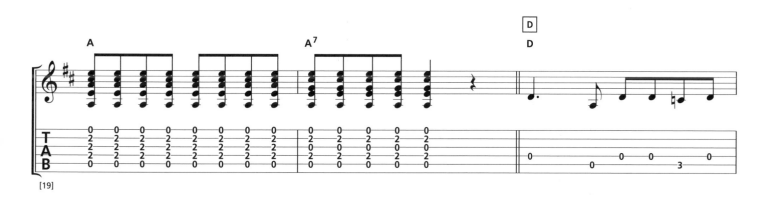

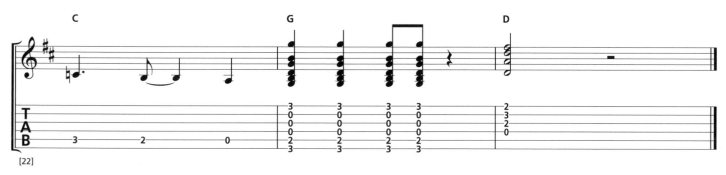

Walkthrough

Amp Settings

Aim for a bright, clean sound. You can boost the treble (and possibly the middle) a small amount if you feel your tone needs a little more bite. If you have a guitar fitted with humbuckers, try using the bridge pickup to keep the sound as bright as possible. Keeping the gain low will ensure that the chords won't distort as you strum. Adding some reverb will help you to achieve the vintage 1960s pop sound.

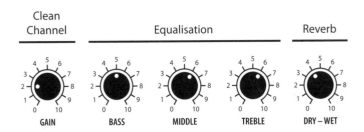

A Section (Bars 1–8)

The A section of 'Fab Stomp' consists of a single-note melody in open position. Dotted note values are the basis of a lot of the phrases.

Bars 1–2 | *Dotted rhythms*

If this is the first time you have encountered dotted rhythms, one way to double-check you are playing the notes in the correct place is to count along to the music. You should count "1 & 2 & 3 & 4 &". The first note is played when you say, "1" and the second note should be played on the "&" of beat 2 (Fig. 1).

B Section (Bars 9–12)

The guitar part in this section of the song is based on a 'question and answer' idea, where the guitar plays two open chords followed by a syncopated (offbeat) rhythm on the E and B strings.

Bars 10–12 | *Double-stops*

A double-stop is two notes played at the same time. The challenge here is to make sure both notes ring out clearly when played. Using the tips of your fingers to fret the notes on the B string will make it easier to arch your finger over the open string. You can check that both notes are ringing by picking them individually.

Bars 10–12 | *Syncopation*

When a part accents the weaker beats in the bar (usually the '&' of each beat) this is known as syncopation. The rhythm in bar 10 may look intimidating. One approach is to work out where each note falls in the bar (Fig. 2) and count "1 & 2 & 3 & 4 &" as you play. Start slowly and only increase speed when you feel you are ready.

C & D Sections (Bars 13–24)

The first half of the C section is a single-note melody in open position, while the second half starts with a two-note powerchord that gradually builds to a full, five string dominant^7 chord. This creates tension that is resolved by the reprise of the opening melody in the D section

Bars 17–18 | A^5 *chord*

Technically, the A^5 chord in bars 16 and 17 is a different chord to the A chord that follows it in bar 19. However, you can save wasting motion by fretting the A chord and simply playing the two lowest sounding strings; this is the essence of an A^5 chord. If you choose to do this, though, you must be careful not to strum too many strings and play the full A chord by accident.

Bar 20 | *Fretting accuracy*

The essential part of this section is that the open G string in the A^7 chord sounds clearly. Check your fretting accuracy by picking the notes individually. If any of the notes don't ring out, adjust your hand position until each of them rings clearly. You may have to adjust your thumb too because this has a large impact on your ability to move your fingers easily.

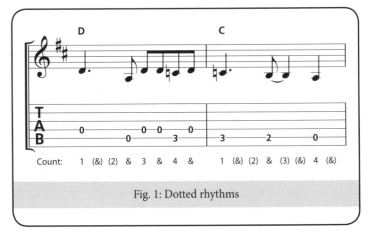

Fig. 1: Dotted rhythms

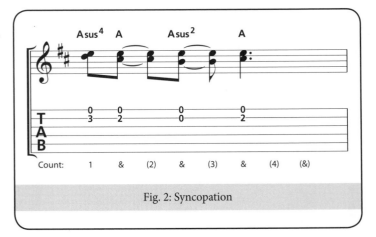

Fig. 2: Syncopation

Technical Exercises

In this section the examiner will ask you to play a selection of exercises drawn from each of the three groups shown below. Groups A and B contain examples of the scales and chords you can use when playing the pieces. In Group C you will be asked to prepare the riff exercise and play it to the backing track in the exam. You do not need to memorise the exercises (and can use the book in the exam) but the examiner will be looking for the speed of your response. The examiner will also give credit for the level of your musicality.

Groups A and B should be prepared as indicated below. Before you start the section you will be asked whether you would like to play the exercises along with the click or hear a single bar of click before you commence the test. The tempo is ♩=70.

Group A: Scales
1. C major scale

2. A natural minor scale

3. E minor pentatonic scale

4. A minor pentatonic scale

5. G major pentatonic

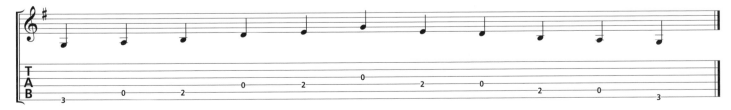

Technical Exercises

Group B: Chords

1. Powerchords: two-note chords to be played in a continuous sequence.

2. Major chords: individual chords will be strummed once as directed by the examiner.

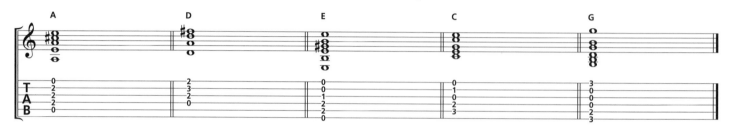

3. Minor chords: individual chords will be strummed once as directed by the examiner.

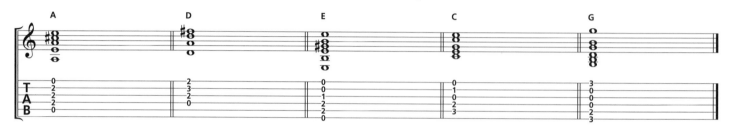

Group C: Riff

In the exam you will be asked to play the following riff to a backing track. The riff shown in bar 1 should be played in the same shape in bars 2–4. The root note of the pattern to be played is shown in the music in each of the subsequent three bars. The tempo is ♩=70.

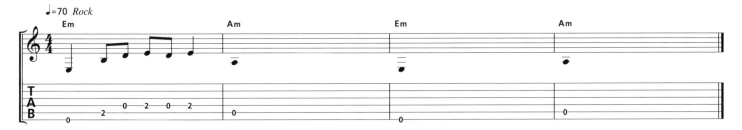

Sight Reading

In this section you have a choice between either a sight reading test or an improvisation and interpretation test (see facing page). You will be asked to prepare a sight reading test which will be given to you by the examiner. The test is a four bar melody in the key of A minor. The examiner will allow you 90 seconds to prepare it and will set the tempo for you. The tempo is ♩=70.

Improvisation & Interpretation

You will be asked to play an improvised line to a backing track of four bars in the keys of either C major or A minor. You may choose to play either rhythmic chords (first CD track) or a melodic lead line (second CD track). You have 30 seconds to prepare and then you will be allowed to practise during the first playing of the backing track before playing it to the examiner on the second playing of the backing track. This test is continuous with a one bar count-in at the beginning and after the practice session. The tempo is ♩ = 70–80.

Ear Tests

There are two ear tests in this grade. The examiner will play each test to you twice. You will find one example of each type of test printed below.

Test 1: Melodic Recall

The examiner will play you three notes in sequence. You will identify whether the notes are higher or lower (up or down) in sequence. You will hear the test twice.

Each time the test is played it is preceded by a one bar vocal count-in. The tempo is ♩ = 85.

Candidate may answer either: "higher/lower" or "up/down".

Test 2: Rhythmic Recall

The examiner will play you a two bar rhythm played to a drum backing on the lowest-sounding E string. You will hear the test twice. You will be asked to play the rhythm back. You will then be asked to identify the rhythm from two printed examples shown to you.

Each time the test is played it is preceded by a one bar count-in. There will be a short gap for you to practise. Next you will hear a *vocal* count-in and you will then play the rhythm to the drum backing. The tempo is ♩ = 90.

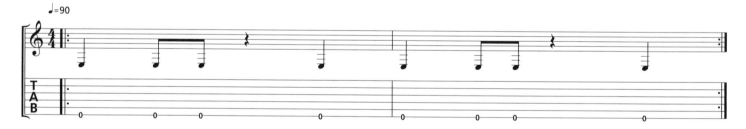

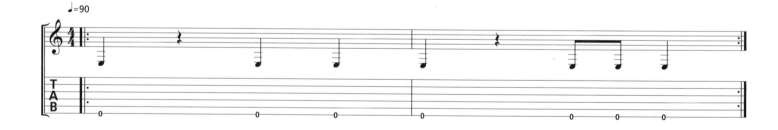

General Musicianship Questions

In this part of the exam you will be asked five questions. Four of these questions will be about general music knowledge and the fifth question will be asked about your instrument.

Music Knowledge
The examiner will ask you four music knowledge questions based on a piece of music that you have played in the exam. You will nominate the piece of music about which the questions will be asked.

In Grade 1 you will be asked to identify:

- The treble clef

- The time signature

- Whole, half, quarter and eighth note values

- The difference between a major and minor chord

Instrument Knowledge
The examiner will also ask you one question regarding your instrument.

In Grade 1 you will be asked to identify:

- The following parts of your guitar: neck, fretboard, body, tuning-pegs, nut, pick-ups and bridge

- One main guitar make other than that of the guitar you are playing

- Names of the open strings

Further Information
Tips on how to approach this part of this exam can be found in the *Syllabus Guide* for guitar, the Rockschool *Guitar Companion Guide* and on the Rockschool website: *www.rockschool.co.uk*.

Entering Rockschool Exams

Entering a Rockschool exam is easy. You may enter either online at *www.rockschool.co.uk* or by downloading and filling in an exam entry form. Information on current exam fees can be obtained from Rockschool online or by calling +44 (0)845 460 4747.

- You should enter for your exam when you feel ready.

- You may enter for any one of the three examination periods shown below with their closing dates:

EXAMINATION PERIODS

PERIOD	DURATION	CLOSING DATE
Period A	1st February to 31st March	1st December
Period B	1st May to 31st July	1st April
Period C	23rd October to 15th December	1st October

These dates apply from 1st September 2012 until further notice

- The full Rockschool examination terms and conditions can be downloaded from our website. The information shown below is a summary.

- Please complete your entry with the information required. Fill in the type and level of exam and instrument, along with the examination period and year. Paper entry forms should be sent with a cheque or postal order (payable to Rockschool Ltd) to the address shown on the entry form. Entry forms sent by post will be acknowledged either by letter or email, while all entries made online will automatically be acknowledged by email.

- Applications received after the expiry of the closing date, whether made by post or online, may be accepted subject to the payment of a late fee.

- Rockschool will allocate your exam to a specific centre and you will receive notification of the exam showing a date, location and time, as well as advice on what to bring to the centre. We endeavour to give you four weeks notice ahead of your exam date.

- You should inform Rockschool of any cancellations or alterations to the schedule as soon as you can because it may not be possible to transfer entries from one centre, or one period, to another without the payment of an additional fee.

- Please bring your music book and CD to the exam. You may use photocopied music if this helps you avoid awkward page turns. The examiner will sign each book during each examination. Please note, you may be barred from taking an exam if you use someone else's music.

- You should aim to arrive for your exam 15 minutes before the time stated on the schedule. Guitarists and bass players should get ready to enter the exam room by taking their instrument from its case and tuning up. This will help with the smooth running of each exam day.

- Each Grade 1 exam is scheduled to last 15 minutes. You can use a small proportion of this time to set up and check the sound levels.

- You will receive a copy of the examiner's marksheet two to three weeks after the exam. If you have passed you will also receive a Rockschool certificate of achievement.

Guitar Grade 1 Marking Schemes

ELEMENT	PASS	MERIT	DISTINCTION
Performance Piece 1	12–14 out of 20	15–17 out of 20	18+ out of 20
Performance Piece 2	12–14 out of 20	15–17 out of 20	18+ out of 20
Performance Piece 3	12–14 out of 20	15–17 out of 20	18+ out of 20
Technical Exercises	9–10 out of 15	11–12 out of 15	13+ out of 15
Either **Sight Reading** *or* **Improvisation & Interpretation**	6 out of 10	7–8 out of 10	9+ out of 10
Ear Tests	6 out of 10	7–8 out of 10	9+ out of 10
General Musicianship Questions	3 out of 5	4 out of 5	5 out of 5
TOTAL MARKS	**60%+**	**74%+**	**90%+**

PERFORMANCE CERTIFICATES | GRADES 1–8

ELEMENT	PASS	MERIT	DISTINCTION
Performance Piece 1	12–14 out of 20	15–17 out of 20	18+ out of 20
Performance Piece 2	12–14 out of 20	15–17 out of 20	18+ out of 20
Performance Piece 3	12–14 out of 20	15–17 out of 20	18+ out of 20
Performance Piece 4	12–14 out of 20	15–17 out of 20	18+ out of 20
Performance Piece 5	12–14 out of 20	15–17 out of 20	18+ out of 20
TOTAL MARKS	**60%+**	**75%+**	**90%+**

Introduction to Tone

A large part of an effective guitar performance is selecting the right tone. The electric guitar's sound is subject to a wide range of variables, and this guide outlines the basic controls present on most amplifiers as well as the common variations between models. There is also a basic overview of pickups and the effect their location on the guitar has on tone. Finally, it covers the differences between the types of distortion, which is crucial to getting your basic sound right.

At Grade 1 you are only expected to use one tone throughout the song and you do not have to use any additional effects units, although you may use them if you wish. You do not have to use distortion. Remember, at Grade 1 a performance on an acoustic guitar is perfectly acceptable.

Basic amplifier controls

Most amplifiers come with a standard set of controls that are the same as, or very similar to, the diagram below. It's important to understand what each control is and the effect that it has on your guitar's tone.

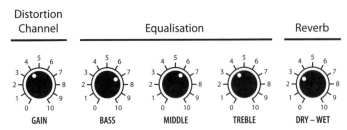

- **Channel (Clean/Distortion)**

  Most amplifiers have two channels that can be selected either by a switch on the amp or a footswitch. One channel is usually 'clean' while the other can be driven harder to create a distorted (or 'dirty') tone. If your amp doesn't have two channels, look at the 'variation of basic controls' below to see how to get clean and dirty tones from a one channel amp.

- **Gain**

  In simple terms, the gain determines how hard you drive the amp. This governs how distorted the dirty (also called 'drive', 'overdrive', or 'distortion') channel is and acts as a second volume control on the clean channel (though a high gain setting will distort even the clean channel).

- **Bass**

  This adjusts the lowest frequencies. Boost it to add warmth and reduce or 'cut' it if your sound is muddy or woolly.

- **Middle**

  This is the most important equalisation (often shortened to just 'EQ') control. Most of the guitar's tonal character is found in the mid-range so adjusting this control has a lot of impact upon your tone. Boosting it with a dirty sound will create a more classic rock tone while cutting it will produce a more metal one.

- **Treble**

  This adjusts the high frequencies. Boost it to add brightness and cut it if the sound is too harsh or brittle.

- **Reverb**

  Short for 'reverberation'. This artificially recreates the ambience of your guitar in a large room, usually a hall. This dial controls the balance between the 'dry' (the sound without the reverb) and 'wet' (the sound with the reverb) sounds.

Variations of basic controls

The diagram above shows the most common amp controls. There are many variations to this basic setup, which can often be confusing. The following section is a breakdown of some of the other amp controls you may encounter:

- **Presence control**

  Sometimes this dial replaces the 'middle' control and other times it appears in addition to it. It adjusts the higher mid-range frequencies (those found between the 'middle' and 'treble' dials).

- **No reverb control**
Reverb can be a nice addition to your guitar tone but it's not essential. Don't be concerned if your amp doesn't have a reverb control.

- **Volume, gain, master setup**
Single channel amplifiers often have an extra volume control (in addition to the master volume) located next to the gain control. For clean sounds, keep the gain set low and the volume similarly low and use the master control for overall volume. If the master control is on 10 and you require more level, turn the volume control up. However, you may find that this starts to distort as you reach the higher numbers.

To get a distorted tone, turn the volume down low and the gain up until you get the amount of distortion you require. Regulate the overall level with master volume. If the master control is on 10 and you require more level simply turn the volume up. In this case, however, you may find you lose clarity before you reach maximum.

Pickups

Entire books have been devoted to the intricacies of pickups. However, three basic pieces of information will help you understand a lot about your guitar tone:

- **Singlecoils**
These narrow pickups are fitted to many guitars. The Fender Stratocaster is the most famous guitar fitted with singlecoils. They produce a bright, cutting sound that can sound a little thin in some situations, especially heavier styles of rock music.

- **Humbuckers**
This type of pickup was originally designed to remove or 'buck' the hum produced by singlecoil pickups, hence the name. They produce a warm, mellow sound compared to singlecoil pickups but have a tendency to sound a little muddy in some situations. They are usually identifiable because they are twice the width of a singlecoil pickup. The Gibson Les Paul is a well-known guitar fitted with humbucking pickups.

- **Pickup location**
Basically, pickups located near the guitar's neck will have the warmest sound and those located near the bridge will have the brightest sound.

Different types of 'dirty' tones

There are lots of different words to describe the 'dirty' guitar sounds. In fact, all the sounds are 'distortions' of the clean tone, which can be confusing when you consider there's a 'type' of distortion called 'distortion'. Below is a simplified breakdown of the three main types of dirty sounds, plus some listening material to help you through this tonal minefield:

- **Overdrive**
This is the mildest form of distortion. It can be quite subtle and only evident when the guitar is played strongly. It can be also be full-on and aggressive.
Hear it on: Cream – 'Sunshine Of Your Love', AC/DC – 'Back In Black', Oasis – 'Cigarettes and Alcohol'.

- **Distortion**
This is usually associated with heavier styles of music. It's dense and the most extreme of the dirty tones and is usually associated with heavy styles of music.
Hear it on: Metallica – 'Enter Sandman', Avenged Sevenfold – 'Bat Country', Bon Jovi – 'You Give Love A Bad Name'.

- **Fuzz**
As the name implies, fuzz is a broken, 'fuzzy' sound. It was popular in the 1960s but, while still evident in certain genres, it's less common now.
Hear it on: Jimi Hendrix Experience – 'Purple Haze', The Kinks – 'You Really Got Me'.

Guitar Grade 1

Guitar Notation Explained

THE MUSICAL STAVE shows pitches and rhythms and is divided by lines into bars. Pitches are named after the first seven letters of the alphabet.

TABLATURE graphically represents the guitar fingerboard. Each horizontal line represents a string and each number represents a fret.

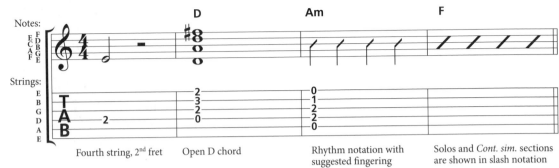

Fourth string, 2nd fret   Open D chord   Rhythm notation with suggested fingering   Solos and *Cont. sim.* sections are shown in slash notation

Definitions For Special Guitar Notation

HAMMER-ON: Pick the lower note, then sound the higher note by fretting it without picking.

PULL-OFF: Pick the higher note then sound the lower note by lifting the finger without picking.

SLIDE: Pick the first note and slide to the next. If the line connects (as below) the second note is *not* repicked.

GLISSANDO: Slide off of a note at the end of its rhythmic value. The note that follows *is* repicked.

STRING BENDS: Pick the first note then bend (or release the bend) to the pitch indicated in brackets.

VIBRATO: Vibrate the note by bending and releasing the string smoothly and continuously.

TRILL: Rapidly alternate between the two bracketed notes by hammering on and pulling off.

NATURAL HARMONICS: Lightly touch the string above the indicated fret then pick to sound a harmonic.

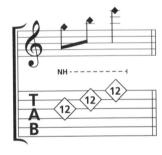

PINCHED HARMONICS: Bring the thumb of the picking hand into contact with the string immediately after the pick.

PICK-HAND TAP: Strike the indicated note with a finger from the picking hand. Usually followed by a pull-off.

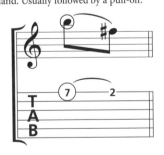

FRET-HAND TAP: As pick-hand tap, but use fretting hand. Usually followed by a pull-off or hammer-on.

QUARTER-TONE BEND: Pick the note indicated and bend the string up by a quarter tone.

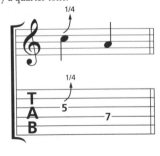

PRE-BENDS: Before picking the note, bend the string from the fret indicated between the staves, to the equivalent pitch indicated in brackets in the TAB.

WHAMMY BAR BEND: Use the whammy bar to bend notes to the pitches indicated in brackets in the TAB.

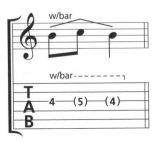

D.%. al Coda

D.C. al Fine

- Go back to the sign (%), then play until the bar marked **To Coda** ⊕ then skip to the section marked ⊕ **Coda**.

- Go back to the beginning of the song and play until the bar marked **Fine** (end).

- Repeat the bars between the repeat signs.

- When a repeated section has different endings, play the first ending only the first time and the second ending only the second time.

SONG TITLE: SKA'D FOR LIFE
GENRE: SKA
TEMPO: 102 BPM
KEY: D MINOR

TECH FEATURES: ARPEGGIATED CHORDS
STACCATO RHYTHMS
HEAVY PALM MUTING

COMPOSER: KIT MORGAN

PERSONNEL: STUART RYAN (GTR)
HENRY THOMAS (BASS)
NOAM LEDERMAN (DRUMS)
FULL PHAT HORNS (BRASS)

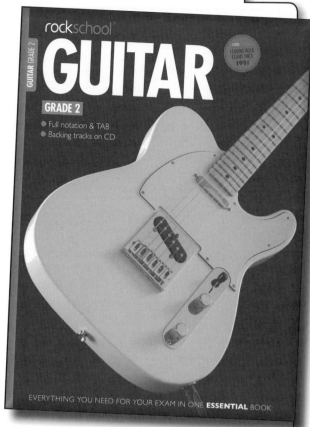

OVERVIEW

'Ska'd For Life' is based on British ska of the late 1970s/early 1980s and the later ska of the American scene that was inspired by it.

STYLE FOCUS

Ska first emerged in Jamaica in the early 1960s. The country was newly independent from Great Britain and a wave of optimism swept the island. This mood was expressed in the new sound of ska, an uptempo style of music with an emphasis on the offbeat (the '&' when you count, "1 & 2 & 3 & 4 &"). In fact, the word ska comes from the sound this emphasis produces; to take the guitar as an example, chords are played on the offbeat then quickly muted by relaxing your grip on the frets for a staccato effect. Jamaican ska is usually written in a major key. However, many songs from the American scene are set in minor keys and with slower tempos.

THE BIGGER PICTURE

Vocalists Desmond Dekker, Prince Buster and Derrick Morgan were great exponents of Jamaican ska, but the genre owed as much to its instrumental groups such as The Skatalites (who backed Prince Buster and others) as it did its singers. Jamaican music was influenced heavily by the output of American radio stations, which could be heard on the island. Jazz, R&B and soul were among the most popular styles, so brass instruments were naturally a feature of ska.

Horn sections were less evident on releases by Coventry's 2 Tone label, home of ska's second wave of the late 1970s and bands like The Specials and The Beat. These young English groups were inspired by the spirit of punk and so the electric guitar became more a focus of their sound.

2 Tone, in turn, inspired a wave of American ska. Groups such as The Mighty Mighty Bosstones and Fishbone pushed the brass back to the fore, while bands like Sublime, Rancid and No Doubt relied on bass, guitar and drums as backing.

RECOMMENDED LISTENING

The Jamaican ska scene was dominated by singles, in a time before the album became rock's – and by extension reggae's – format of choice. A compilation such as *Trojan Presents Ska* will offer you a sample of all the major artists of the era. The Specials' eponymous debut album of 1979 epitomises the 2 Tone sound. *Let's Face It* by The Mighty Mighty Bosstones (1997) is a great example of the horn-heavy American style.

Ska'd For Life (Grade 2 Preview)

Kit Morgan

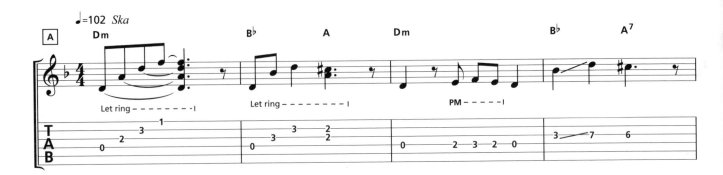

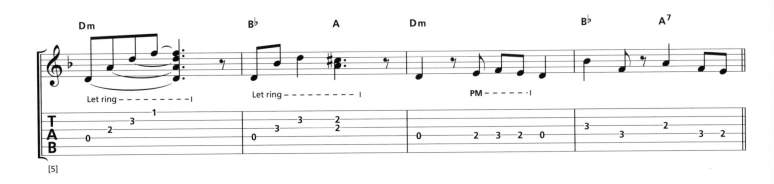

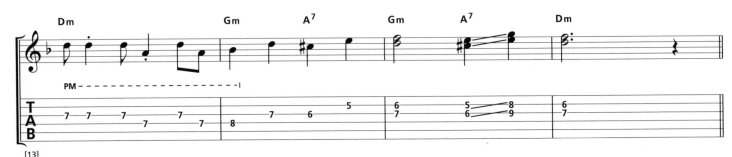

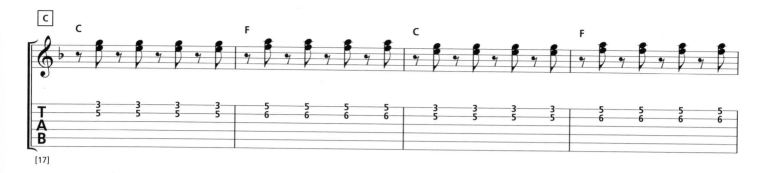

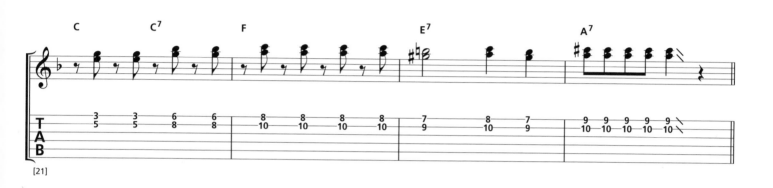

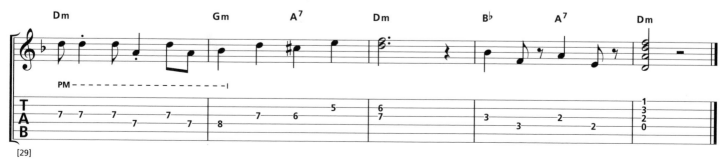

Walkthrough (Grade 2 Preview)

Amp Settings

Although we have suggested an overdriven tone here, a clean tone will work just as well. If you opt for overdrive, use a low gain setting because you're only looking for a small amount of distortion. 'Ska'd For Life' has quite a dense arrangement, so boosting the middle will help the guitar cut through the other instruments.

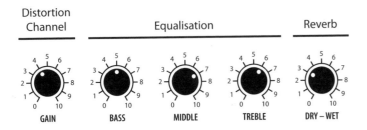

A Section (Bars 1–8)

This section consists of arpeggiated chords and single note lines, some of which are palm-muted.

Bars 1–2 | *Arpeggiated chords*

When the notes of a chord are played individually, this is known as an arpeggio. When the notes of a chord are picked individually, usually so that they ring into each other, the chords are being 'arpeggiated'.

Bar 3 | *Heavy palm-muting*

Place the edge of the outside of your palm on the lowest-sounding strings and press firmly to get the heavy mute required for this part. Be careful not to move your hand too far from the bridge because this may raise the pitch of the note. Take extra care if your guitar has a floating bridge (where the bridge is tensioned to 'float' above the guitar's body) because pressing too hard will push the bridge down and raise the pitch of the notes.

B Section (Bars 9–16)

The B section uses a combination of syncopated, heavily palm-muted riffs and double-stops, two of which are connected with a slide.

Bar 9 | *Staccato open strings*

These open strings are already being palm-muted and will, by their very nature, sound shorter than notated. In order to cut the notes marked as staccato even shorter, you will need to place your pick back on the string to stop it from ringing.

Bar 9 | *Counting rhythms*

Bar 9 is quite an easy rhythm to pick up by ear, but if you find it difficult try counting the bar slowly in eighth notes and carefully place the notes at the right time (Fig. 1). Only increase the speed when you feel comfortable with the part.

Bar 15 | *Sliding double-stops*

Make sure you 'lock' your fingers in position and slide up by moving your whole hand. This will help keep your fingers in the shape they were in when you fretted the first double-stop and stop the finger fretting the G string from moving and accidentally muting the B string. As you slide up, take care to maintain pressure on the strings (imagine you are pushing into the fretboard) so that the notes keep ringing.

C & D Sections (Bars 17–33)

The C section consists of double-stops that outline the accompanying chord progression and are played in a syncopated rhythm typical of this style. The D section is a reprise of the B section with a few variations to bring the piece to a close.

Bars 17–22 | *Syncopated double-stops*

When a part accents the weaker beats in the bar (usually the '&' of each beat), this is known as syncopation. Count along to the music in eighth notes: "1 & 2 & 3 & 4 &". A double-stop is played on the '&' of every beat in these bars. Try to lock into the feel of this groove to make your part sound more musical. You may find it easier to treat this as a rhythm guitar part using a constant strumming motion (Fig. 2).

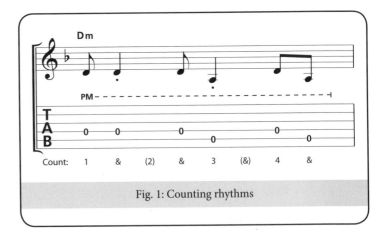

Fig. 1: Counting rhythms

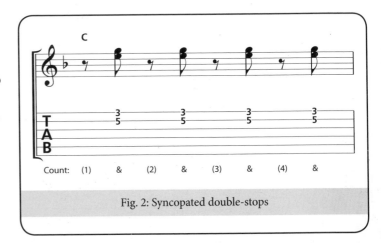

Fig. 2: Syncopated double-stops